Old Dame Trot
& Her Pig

n old Woman, sweeping her house, found a crooked sixpence.

"What," said she, "shall I do with this little sixpence? I will go to market and buy a little Pig."

s she was coming home
she came to a Stile,
but the pig would not
get over the Stile.

She went a little further and she met a Dog. So she said: —

"Dog, Dog, bite Pig!
Pig won't get over the Stile
And I shan't get home to-night."

But the Dog would not.

She went a little further and she met
a Stick. So she said: —

   "Stick, Stick, beat Dog!
      Dog won't bite Pig,
      Pig won't get over the Stile
      And I shan't get home to-night."

But the Stick would not.

She went a little further and she met a Fire. So she said: —

"Fire, Fire, burn Stick!
　　Stick won't beat Dog,
　　Dog won't bite Pig,
　　Pig won't get over the Stile
　　And I shan't get home to-night."

But the Fire would not.

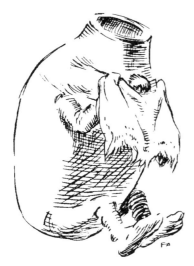

She went a little
further and she met
some Water.
So she said: —

"Water, Water, quench Fire!
Fire won't burn Stick,
Stick won't beat Dog,
Dog won't bite Pig,
Pig won't get over the Stile
And I shan't get home to-night."

But the Water would not.

She went a little further and she met
an Ox. So she said: —

"Ox, Ox, drink Water!
 Water won't quench Fire,
 Fire won't burn Stick,
 Stick won't beat Dog,
 Dog won't bite Pig,
 Pig won't get over the Stile
 And I shan't get home to-night."

FRANK ADAMS

But the Ox would not!

She went a little further and she met
a Butcher. So she said: —

"Butcher, Butcher, kill Ox!
   Ox won't drink Water,
   Water won't quench Fire,
   Fire won't burn Stick,
   Stick won't beat Dog,
   Dog won't bite Pig,
   Pig won't get over the Stile
   And I shan't get home to-night."

But the Butcher
   would not.

She went a little further and she met a Rope. So she said: —

> "Rope, Rope, hang Butcher!
> Butcher won't kill Ox,
> Ox won't drink Water,
> Water won't quench Fire,
> Fire won't burn Stick,
> Stick won't beat Dog,
> Dog won't bite Pig,
> Pig won't get over the Stile
> And I shan't get home to-night."

But the Rope would not.

She went a little further and she met
a Rat. So she said: —

"Rat, Rat, gnaw Rope!
Rope won't hang Butcher,
Butcher won't kill Ox,
Ox won't drink Water,
Water won't quench Fire,
Fire won't burn Stick,
Stick won't beat Dog,
Dog won't bite Pig,
Pig won't get over the Stile
And I shan't get home to-night."

But the Rat would not.

She went a little further and she met a Cat. So she said: —

"Cat, Cat, kill Rat!
   Rat won't gnaw Rope,
   Rope won't hang Butcher,
   Butcher won't kill Ox,
   Ox won't drink Water,
   Water won't quench Fire,
   Fire won't burn Stick,
   Stick won't beat Dog,
   Dog won't bite Pig,
   Pig won't get over the Stile
   And I shan't get home to-night."

The Cat said: "If you will
give me a saucer of milk,
I will kill the Rat."

So the old Woman gave
the Cat the milk and when
she had lapped it up —

The Cat began to kill the Rat,
The Rat began to gnaw the Rope,
The Rope began to hang the Butcher,
The Butcher began to kill the Ox,
The Ox began to drink the Water,
The Water began to quench the Fire,
The Fire began to burn the Stick,
The Stick began to beat the Dog,
The Dog began to bite the Pig,
The Pig jumped over the Stile,

And so the old Woman
got home that night.